Port to

It is the morning of the fun run. I have on my vest and sports shorts. I am set to go!

Port To Fort Run

The run starts at the port
and ends at the fort.
If you win, you get a cup.

Run north to the fort and keep on the track. There will be lots of wind but no storm.

A man sorts us out for the start.

I start out too hard.
I huff and puff and snort.
Soon I am worn out.

I go down the track to
a farm. There is corn
as far as I can see.

Rip!

Then I run into a garden.
My shorts get stuck on a
thorn. Rip! They are torn.

I have to stop. My shorts
are flapping in the wind.

I dart to the back of the
shrub. My shorts drop right off!

I pick up my shorts. A big gust of wind sweeps them out of my hands.

I am standing in my moon and stars pants! I groan.

Then I see a long scarf
floating in the wind. It
gets stuck on a thorn, too.

I grab the scarf. I tuck
it into my pants and
rush back to the track.

I stop thinking of the cup
and winning the fun run.
I just need to finish.

I get to the fort and Mum
and Dad meet me with a
big hug.

I do not win the fun run
but I still get a cup.
I am "The Best Dressed".

Words to blend

starts	keep	hard
farm	far	garden
moon	star	dart
shrub	sweeps	groan
scarf	rush	finish
meet	woo-hoo	thinking
too	need	soon

Before reading

Synopsis: Sam is doing a fun run from the port to the fort. He starts off well but feels worn out so goes across a corn field and tears his shorts on rose thorns.

Review phoneme/s: ar

New phoneme: or

Story discussion: Look at the cover, and read the title together. Ask: *What do you think Sam is doing? Is there anything unusual about what he's wearing? Why do you think this book is called* Port to fort? Help children read the race banner on the cover, which is partly obscured by Sam's hands.

Link to prior learning: Display the grapheme *or*. Remind children that digraphs are two letters that make one sound together. Can they read the grapheme and say the sound? Ask children to find three words with *or* on page 7 (*shorts, thorn, torn*).

Vocabulary check: Dart – run fast. Say: *Dart can have two meanings. It can mean a sharp thing a bit like an arrow, or it can mean to run fast.* Show children the sentence with dart on page 9. Which meaning do they think the word has here?

Decoding practice: Display the word *torn*. How many rhyming words can children think of? (e.g. born, corn, horn, torn, worn) Write the suggested words on cards and mix them up. Challenge children to read them.

Tricky word practice: Display the word *are*. Say it out loud and ask children to find the letters that make the /ar/ sound (ar). Circle the e at the end and point out that it doesn't add to the sound (it is silent). Give children opportunities to practise writing this word and look out for it when reading.

After reading

Apply learning: Briefly recap the story and talk about how Sam's feelings changed, from excitement at the start of the race, to feeling worn out, feeling worried and embarrassed about his torn shorts, having the clever idea about the scarf, and finally his relief at finishing the race. Children could help you draw a feelings graph with a line showing how his feelings rise at the good points in the story and fall when bad things happen.

Comprehension

- What places does Sam run through on his way to the fort?

- Why is Sam so embarrassed when his shorts get torn?

- Sam gets a cup at the end of the race. Did he win the race?

Fluency

- Pick a page that most of the group read quite easily. Ask them to reread it with pace and expression. Model how to do this if necessary.

- Turn to page 8, and ask children to read Sam's thought bubble with lots of expression, to show how he feels. Demonstrate this if necessary.

- Practise reading the words on page 17.

Tricky words review

my	of	have
me	go	you
there	be	as
out	into	they
are	oh	do